First Comes
RED

Meredith Costain
Illustrated by Tracie Grimwood

First comes **red**.
Red is the color of the apples
on the tree.
I like red.

Next comes orange.
Orange is the color of the chair
that I sit on.
I like orange.

Next comes yellow.
Yellow is the color of the sun
in the sky.
I like yellow.

Next comes green.
Green is the color of the grass
in the park.
I like green.

Next comes blue.
Blue is the color of the water
in the bay.
I like blue.

Next comes **indigo**.
Indigo is the color of the shirt
that I wear.
I like indigo.

Last comes **violet**.
Violet is the color of the flowers
in our garden.
I like violet.

Look. I've made a rainbow!
How beautiful!